A DUCK IS A DUCK

THEODORE CLYMER: SENIOR AUTHOR

GINN AND COMPANY

A XEROX COMPANY

CONTRIBUTING AUTHORS

DORIS GATES
ELEANOR G. ROBISON
ELIZABETH F. RUSSELL

CONSULTANTS

ROGER W. SHUY · LINGUISTICS
E. PAUL TORRANCE · CREATIVITY

ARTISTS • ROBERT AMUNDSEN, GEORGE GUZZI

0−663−25155−9

CONTENTS

THE PARK

AT THE PARK

This is Bill.

Bill is at the park.

Here is Jill.
Jill is at the park.

Here is Ben.

Ben is at the park.

Is Lad at the park?

THE DUCKS

Bill said, "Look here, Ben.
Look at the ducks."

Ben said, "Here, ducks.
Look here.
Get this, ducks."

Jill said, "Look, Bill.
Look at Ben and the ducks."

Ben said, "Here is a duck.
The duck can get this."

Ben said, " Stop, ducks.
Stop this, ducks ! "

Jill said, "Help Ben.

Stop the ducks, Bill.

Help Ben stop the ducks."

LAD

Jill said, "Bill! Bill!
Lad will get the ducks.
Bill, stop Lad."

Bill said, "Here, Lad.
No, Lad! No!"

Jill said, "No, Lad!
Stop! Stop!"

18

Ben said, "Here, Lad.
Look at this.
Get this, Lad."

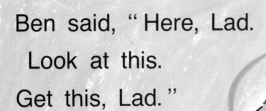

Bill said, "Jill, look here.
Ben can help.
Ben can get Lad.
Lad will not get the ducks."

Ben said, "Stop, Bill.
Can we eat here?"

Jill said, "Can we, Bill?
Can we eat here?"

Bill said, "Yes, Jill.
We will eat here."

20

Ben said, " Stop, ducks !
You can't eat this.
No, you can't !

No, ducks ! No !
You can't eat this. "

21

Bill said, "Lad will help.
Lad will stop the ducks."

Ben said, "Run, ducks! Run!
You can't eat here.
Lad will stop you."

Bill said, "Here, Lad.
You can eat this.
Eat this, Lad."

Ben said, "Yes, Lad.
You can eat this.
We will not stop you."

BEN'S RIDE

Ben said, "Look at me, Jill.
Look at me!"

Jill said, " Yes, Ben.
You can ride. "

Ben said, "Help me! Help me!
I can't stop!
I can't stop this!"

Jill said, "Ben can't stop.
Run, Bill.
Run and help Ben."

Bill said, "I can stop this.
Jill and I will help you, Ben."

Jill said, "Yes, Ben.
We can help you."

27

Ben said, "Will you ride, Jill?
Will you ride with me?"

Jill said, "Yes, Ben.
I will ride here with you.
Bill and I will help you."

Jill

will

is

with

this

Bill

Is this Jill ?

Is Jill with Bill ?

This page provides for recognition of the
unglided vowel sound /i/ and its correspondence
with the vowel letter *i* in known words.

29

WHAT IS IT ?

31

What Can Hide?

Bill said, "No, Lad.
You can't come with me."

Ben said, "Come here, Lad.
Come here!"

Jill said, "Look, Bill.
Look at Lad."

34

Ben said, "What is it, Lad?
What is it?"

Bill said, "It is a turtle!
Look at the turtle, Ben."

Ben said, "A turtle!

It can hide.

This turtle can hide."

37

The  TURTLE

Bill said, "Come here, Ted.
Come and see what is here."

Ben said, "It is a turtle!
Come and see it, Ted.
The turtle can hide."

Ted said, "A turtle?
You see turtles at the park!
I want to see this."

Bill said, "Here it is, Ted.
Here is the turtle.
We want you to see it."

40

Jill said, "Come here, Nan.
See what is here."

Nan said, "A turtle!
I want to see it."

Ted said, "Come with me, Turtle.
Lad will get you here.
I will help you."

Bill said, "Come, Nan and Jill.
Come with Ted and me.
We will help this turtle."

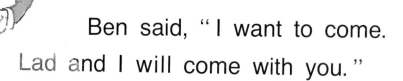

Ben said, "I want to come.
Lad and I will come with you."

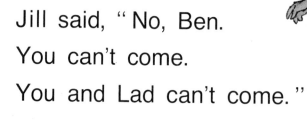

Jill said, "No, Ben.
You can't come.
You and Lad can't come."

CAN YOU GUESS?

Today is Tuesday

Ted said, "Guess what is here.
Will you guess, Miss Hill?"

Miss Hill said, "Yes, Ted.
I will guess.
Will you help me guess?"

43

Jill said, "It is little.

Can you guess, Miss Hill?

What is little?"

Miss Hill said, "It is little.

What is little?

Is it this?"

Nan said, "It is little.
It can hide.
Can you guess, Miss Hill?"

Miss Hill said, "It is little.
What is little and can hide?
Is it this?"

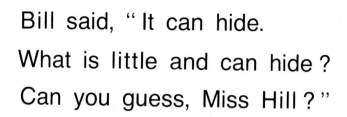

Bill said, "It can hide.
What is little and can hide?
Can you guess, Miss Hill?"

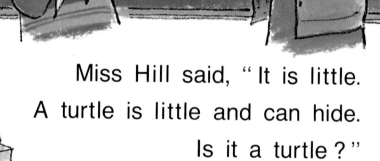

Miss Hill said, "It is little.
A turtle is little and can hide.
Is it a turtle?"

Ted said, "It is! It is!
Here is the turtle, Miss Hill!"

Jill said, "The turtle is little.
We want to help it.
What can we do ?"

Miss Hill said, "We will see.
What do you want to do ?"

Ted wants to do this.

Bill wants to do this.

Nan wants to do this.

Jill wants to do this.

48

Jill said, "Look here, turtle.
What do you want?
What do turtles like to do?"

Nan said, "Turtles like to hide.
Turtles like to eat.
But what will this turtle eat?"

Bill said, "Turtles like to swim.
But this turtle can't swim here."

49

Ted said, "We can help the turtle.
It can't swim here.
But it can swim at the park."

Nan said, "This turtle is little.
Will it like the park?"

Miss Hill said, "You can see.
Run to the park with the turtle.
See what it will do."

A Park Turtle

Jill said, "Here, little turtle.
I will help you."

Nan said, "Swim, little turtle.
We want to see you swim."

Ted said, "The turtle can swim!
It likes to swim here."

Jill said, "Don't hide, turtle.
　　　　I want to see you swim.
I don't want you to hide."

Nan said, "Will the turtle eat?
It can swim here.
But what will it eat?"

Bill said, "It wants to eat.
Don't you see, Nan?
Don't you see what it wants?"

Nan said, "I can see.
I see what the turtle wants.
It will eat at the park."

Jill said, "Guess what!
This is a park turtle."

Ted said, "It will like the park.
We can come here to see it."

In the Park

Ted likes to hike.

Jill sits with Nan.

Bill rides a bike.

What can Ben hit ?

ride	like	Bill	it
hide	bike	hill	bit
wide	hike	mill	hit
side	Mike	will	sit

This page provides for recognition and reinforcement of the vowel correspondence /i/*i* as in *hill* and the vowel correspondence /ay/*i__e* as in *side* through the decoding of new words.   55

HELP ME READ

Ben said, "I want to read.
I will read this book."

Bill said, "Can you read, Ben?
Can you read this book?"

Ben said, "I can read.
I can read a little.
But I want you to help me."

Rabbit and Turtle

Rabbit said, "I can run.
I can run fast.
You can't run, Turtle.
You can't run fast."

Turtle said, "Look, Rabbit.
Do you see the park?
You and I will run.
We will run to the park."

Rabbit said, "I want to stop.
I will stop here.
I can run, but Turtle can't.
I can get to the park fast."

Turtle said, "I can't run fast.
But I will not stop.
Rabbit can't see me.
I will get to the park."

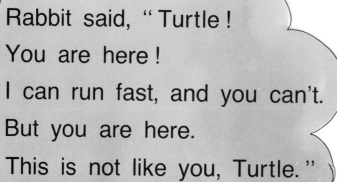

Rabbit said, "Turtle!
You are here!
I can run fast, and you can't.
But you are here.
This is not like you, Turtle."

Turtle said, "I do not stop.
You run fast, Rabbit.
I can't run fast.
But you stop, and I don't."

Little DUCK and Little RABBIT

Little Duck said, "Look at me!
Look at me, Little Rabbit.

I CAN SWIM.

What can you do?

Can you swim, Little Rabbit?"

Little Rabbit said, "Look at me!
Look at me, Little Duck.

I CAN HOP.

I CAN HOP FAST.

Can you do this?
Can you hop, Little Duck?"

Little Duck said, "I can't hop.
I can swim, but I can't hop.
I don't want to swim.

I want to hop, Little Rabbit.
You can hop fast.
I want to hop like a rabbit."

70

Little Rabbit said, "Help me!
I want to swim, but I can't.
I can hop, but I can't swim.
You can swim, Little Duck.

Help me swim."

Mother Duck said, "Come here.
Come here, Little Duck.
  Come and swim with me.
    You can't hop!

You are not a rabbit.
You are a duck!
Ducks can swim.
Come and swim like a duck."

Mother Rabbit said, "See here!
You are not a duck.

You are a rabbit!

Rabbits can't swim.
Rabbits hop and hop.
Come and hop with me.
Come and hop like a rabbit."

75

A duck is a **duck** and a rabbit is a **rabbit**.

The Library

Boys and girls come to the library
to read books.

What books do you like ?

78 This page provides for vocabulary expansion through the introduction of new words in meaningful context.

• Words in This Book •

Unit I

5. the	can
park	14. stop
6. at	15. help
this	18. will
is	no
Bill	19. not
8. here	20. we
Jill	eat
9. Ben	yes
Lad	21. you
10. duck	can't
11. said	22. run
look	24. ride
12. get	me
13. and	26. I
a	28. with

Unit II

31. what	but
it	swim
32. hide	52. don't
come	
35. turtle	**Unit III**
38. Ted	56. read
see	books
39. want	60. rabbit
to	69. fast
41. Nan	64. are
43. guess	68. hop
Miss	73. Mother
Hill	
44. little	
47. do	
49. like	

To the Teacher: *A Duck Is a Duck*, Level Three, Reading 360, introduces 29 new words and maintains the 29 words presented in *My Sound and Word Book*. The underlined words are those introduced at this level. Plural and possessive forms of words are not listed separately.

• Words for Decoding Practice •

The following words, grouped by similar elements, have been presented in this book.

ill	it	is	iss	i	ide	ike
Bill	it	**is**	Miss	I	**hide**	like
Hill					**ride**	
Jill						
will						

The following words, also grouped by similar elements, may be decoded independently by the pupils, utilizing the skills learned in *A Duck Is A Duck*. Words shown in color were presented on exercise pages of this book. These groupings of words may be used to develop additional decoding lessons. See T. E. for uses.

ill	it	is	iss	ip	in	i	ipe	ide	ike	ile
ill	bit	his	hiss	dip	in	hi	pipe	side	bike	file
dill	fit		kiss	hip	bin		ripe	tide	hike	mile
fill	hit			lip	pin		wipe	wide	Mike	pile
kill	kit			rip	tin					
mill	sit			sip	win			ite	ine
pill				tip					bite	fine
sill				yip					kite	line
till				zip						mine
										pine